Broadway
15 showstoppers for keyboard

All Good Gifts . . . . .from Godspell 2

And All That Jazz . . . . .from Chicago 4

Don't Rain On My Parade . . . . .from Funny Girl 6

Everything's Coming Up Roses . . . . . .from Gypsy 8

Fame! . . . . .from Fame! 10

From This Moment On . . . . .from Kiss Me Kate 12

If I Were A Rich Man . . . . .from Fiddler On The Roof 14

It's The Hard-Knock Life . . . . .from Annie 16

Money Money . . . . .from Cabaret 18

The Rain In Spain . . . . .from My Fair Lady 20

Razzle Dazzle . . . . .from Chicago 22

That's Entertainment . . . . .from The Band Wagon 24

There's No Business Like Show Business .from Annie Get Your Gun 26

Well, Did You Evah . . . . .from High Society 28

With A Little Bit Of Luck . . . . .from My Fair Lady 30

Published 2003

Music arranged & processed by Artemis Music Limited
Cover Image Corbis

© International Music Publications Ltd
Griffin House 161 Hammersmith Road London England W6 8BS

All Good Gifts
(FROM *GODSPELL*)

Words and Music by Stephen Schwartz

Suggested Registration: Flute
Rhythm: Ballad
Tempo: ♩ = 116

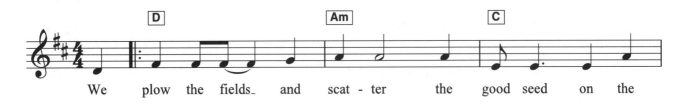

We plow the fields and scat-ter the good seed on the

land, But it is fed and wa-tered by

God's al-might-ty hand. He sends the snow in

win-ter, the warmth to swell the grain, The

breez-es and the sun-shine and soft re-fresh-ing

rain. All good gifts a-round

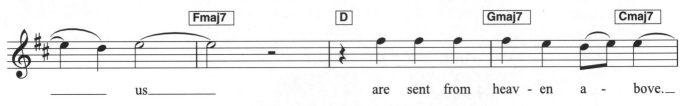

us are sent from heav-en a-bove.

And All that Jazz

(FROM *Chicago*)

Words by John Kander. Music by Fred Ebb

Suggested Registration: Piano
Rhythm: Ragtime
Tempo: ♩ = 112

Come on, babe,_ why don't we paint the town,_ And

all that jazz!_ I'm gon-na rouge my knees_ and roll my stock-ings down_

And all that jazz! Start the car,_ I know a whoop-ee spot_ where the

gin is cold_ but the pi-an-o's hot._ It's just a nois-y hall_ where there's a

night-ly brawl And all that jazz!

Slick your hair_ and wear your buck-le shoes And all that jazz! I hear that

Fa-ther Dip_ is gon-na blow the blues And all that jazz!_

Don't Rain On My Parade

(FROM *FUNNY GIRL*)

Words by Bob Merrill. Music by Jule Styne

Suggested Registration: Trumpet
Rhythm: Bright swing
Tempo: ♩ = 132

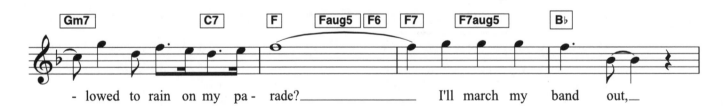

Everything's Coming Up Roses

(FROM *GYPSY*)

Words by Stephen Sondheim. Music by Jule Styne

Suggested Registration: Trumpet
Rhythm: Bright two-beat
Tempo: ♩ = 136

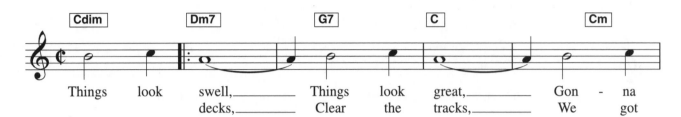

Things look swell,_____ Things look great,_____ Gon - na
decks,_____ Clear the tracks,_____ We got

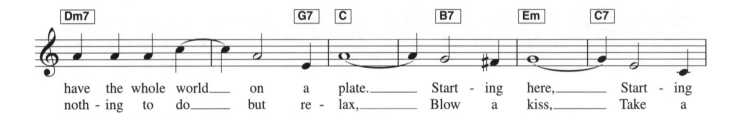

have the whole world_ on a plate._____ Start - ing here,_____ Start - ing
noth - ing to do_____ but re - lax, Blow a kiss,_____ Take a

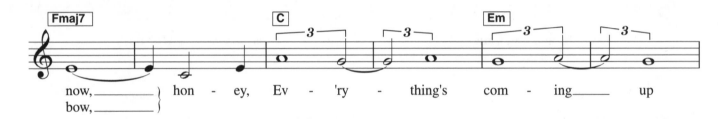

now,_____ } hon - ey, Ev - 'ry - thing's com - ing_____ up
bow,_____ }

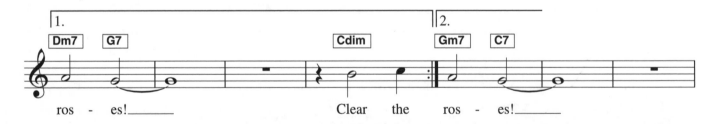

ros - es!_____ Clear the ros - es!

Now's our_ in - ning,_ Stand the world on its ear!

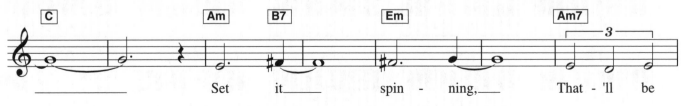

Set it_____ spin - ning,_____ That - 'll be

FAME!
(FROM *FAME!*)

Words by Dean Pitchford. Music by Michael Gore

Suggested Registration: Saxophone
Rhythm: Disco
Tempo: ♩ = 128

Bab - by, look____ at me____ and tell____ me what____

____ you____ see. You ain't seen____ the best____ of me yet. Give me time; I'll make

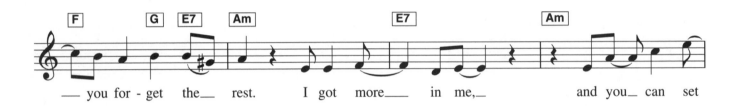

____ you for - get the____ rest. I got more____ in me,____ and you____ can set

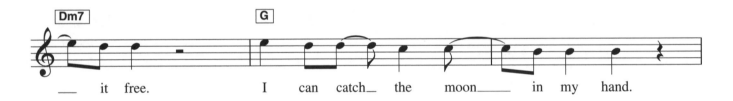

____ it free. I can catch____ the moon____ in my hand.

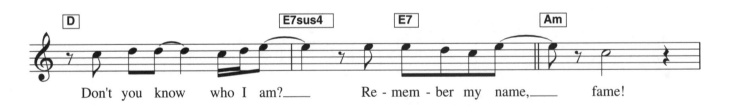

Don't you know who I am?____ Re - mem - ber my name,____ fame!

I'm gon - na live____ for - ev - er. I'm gon - na learn how to fly____ high!

I feel it com - in' to - ge - ther. Peo - ple will see____ me and die.

From This Moment On

(FROM *KISS ME KATE*)

Words and Music by Cole Porter

Suggested Registration: Violin
Rhythm: Bright show style
Tempo: ♩ = 124

If I Were A Rich Man

(FROM FIDDLER ON THE ROOF)

Words by Sheldon Harnick. Music by Jerry Bock

Suggested Registration: Banjo
Rhythm: Ballad
Tempo: ♩ = 112

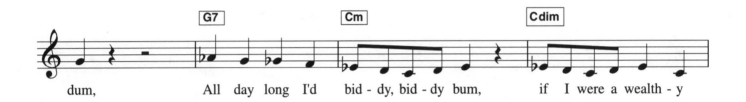

If I were a rich man, dai - dle, dee - dle, dai - dle, dig - guh, dig - guh, dee - dle, dai - dle,

dum, All day long I'd bid - dy, bid - dy bum, if I were a wealth - y

man. Would - n't have to work hard, dai - dle, dee - dle, dai - dle,

dig - guh, dig - guh, dee - dle, dai - dle, dum. If I were a bid - dy, bid - dy rich,

dai - dle, dee - dle, dai - dle, dai - dle man. I'd build a big tall house with

rooms by the doz - en right in the mid - dle of the town, A fine tin roof with

real wood - en floors be - low. There would be one long stair - case just go - ing up and

It's The Hard-Knock Life

(FROM *ANNIE*)

Words by Martin Charnin. Music by Charles Strouse

Suggested Registration: Clarinet
Rhythm: Show style swing
Tempo: ♩= 144

It's the hard - knock life for us! It's the hard - knock life for us!

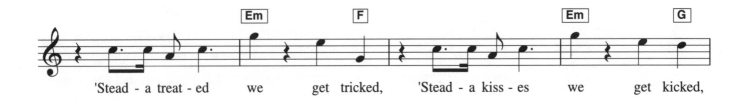

'Stead - a treat - ed we get tricked, 'Stead - a kiss - es we get kicked,

It's the hard - knock life! Got no folks to speak of, so,___

___ It's the hard - knock row we hoe.___ Cot - ton blan - kets 'stead - a wool,

___ Emp - ty bel - lies 'stead - a full,___ It's the hard - knock life.

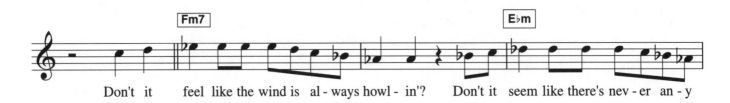

Don't it feel like the wind is al - ways howl - in'? Don't it seem like there's nev - er an - y

light? Once a day don't you want to throw the towel in? It's eas - i - er than put - tin' up a

Money Money
(FROM *Cabaret*)

Words by Fred Ebb. Music by John Kander

Suggested Registration: Piano
Rhythm: Bright swing
Tempo: ♩ = 152

Mon - ey makes the world go a - round, the world go a - round, the world go a - round,
mark, a yen, a buck or a pound, a buck or a pound, a buck or a pound

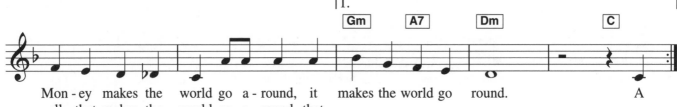

Mon - ey makes the world go a - round, it makes the world go round. A
all that makes the world go a - round, that

clink - ing, clank - ing sound can make the world go round. If you hap - pen to be

rich, and you feel like a night's en - ter - tain - ment, you can pay for a gay es - ca -

pade. If you hap - pen to be rich, and a - lone, and you need a com - pan - ion, you can

ring ting - a - ling for the maid. If you hap - pen to be rich and you find you are

left by your lov - er, tho' you moan and you groan quite a lot, you can take it on the

The Rain In Spain

(FROM *My Fair Lady*)

Words by Alan Jay Lerner. Music by Frederick Loewe

Suggested Registration: Violin
Rhythm: Habanera
Tempo: ♩ = 132

The rain in Spain stays main - ly in the plain._____ I think she's

got it._____ I think she's got it._____ The rain in Spain stays

main - ly in the plain._____ By George, she's got it!_____ By George, she's

got it!_____ Now once a - gain, where does it rain? On the plain! On the

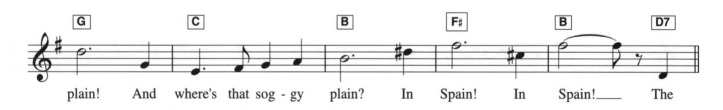

plain! And where's that sog - gy plain? In Spain! In Spain!_____ The

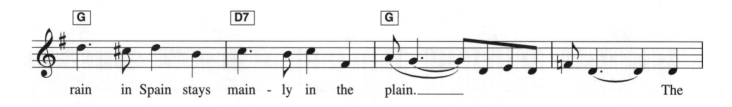

rain in Spain stays main - ly in the plain._____ The

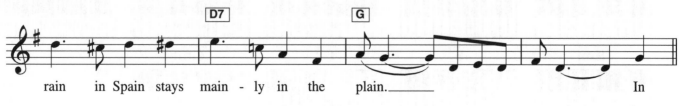

rain in Spain stays main - ly in the plain._____ In

Razzle Dazzle

(FROM *CHICAGO*)

Words by John Kander. Music by Fred Ebb

Suggested Registration: Trumpet
Rhythm: Swing
Tempo: ♩ = 104

That's Entertainment
(FROM *THE BAND WAGON*)

Words by Howard Dietz. Music by Arthur Schwartz

Suggested Registration: Trumpet
Rhythm: Bright show style
Tempo: ♩ = 120

The clown_____ with his pants fall-ing down,_____ Or the dance_____

_____ that's a dream of ro-mance,_____ Or the scene_____ where the

vil-lain is mean;_____ That's en-ter-tain-ment!_____ The

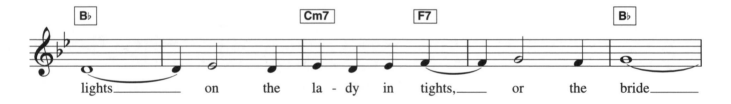

lights_____ on the la-dy in tights,_____ or the bride_____

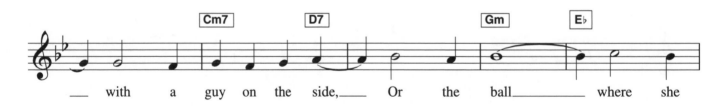

_____ with a guy on the side,_____ Or the ball_____ where she

gives him her all,_____ That's en-ter-tain-ment!_____

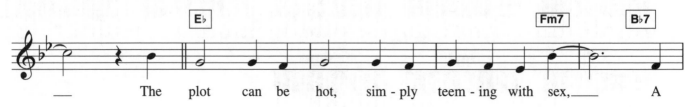

_____ The plot can be hot, sim-ply teem-ing with sex,_____ A

There's No Business Like Show Business

(FROM *Annie Get Your Gun*)

Words and Music by Irving Berlin

Suggested Registration: Brass
Rhythm: Bright show style
Tempo: ♩ = 132

Well, Did You Evah
(FROM *HIGH SOCIETY*)

Words and Music by Cole Porter

Suggested Registration: Clarinet
Rhythm: Polka
Tempo: ♩ = 72

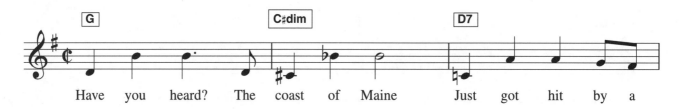

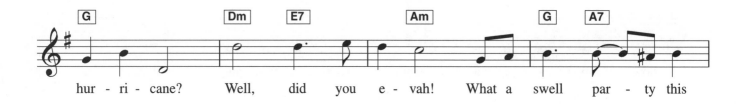

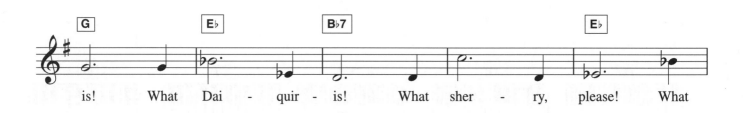

WITH A LITTLE BIT OF LUCK

(FROM *MY FAIR LADY*)

Words by Alan Jay Lerner. Music by Frederick Loewe

Suggested Registration: Saxophone
Rhythm: Bright show style
Tempo: ♩ = 120

An expansive series of over 50 titles!

Each song features melody line, vocals, chord displays, suggested registrations and rhythm settings.

"For each title ALL the chords (both 3 finger and 4 finger) used are shown in
the correct position - which makes a change!" **Organ & Keyboard Cavalcade, May 2001**

Each song appears on two facing pages eliminating the need to turn the page during performance.
We have just introduced a new cover look to the series and will repackage the backlist in the same way.

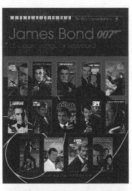